First published in the UK in 2019 by Tiny Owl Publishing, London

www.tinyowl.co.uk

A catalogue record for this book is available from the British Library.

ISBN 978-1-910328-42-2

Printed in China

DARE

LORNA GUTIERREZ

POLLY NOAKES

TINY OWL

Dare to *dream*.
Dare to *aspire*.

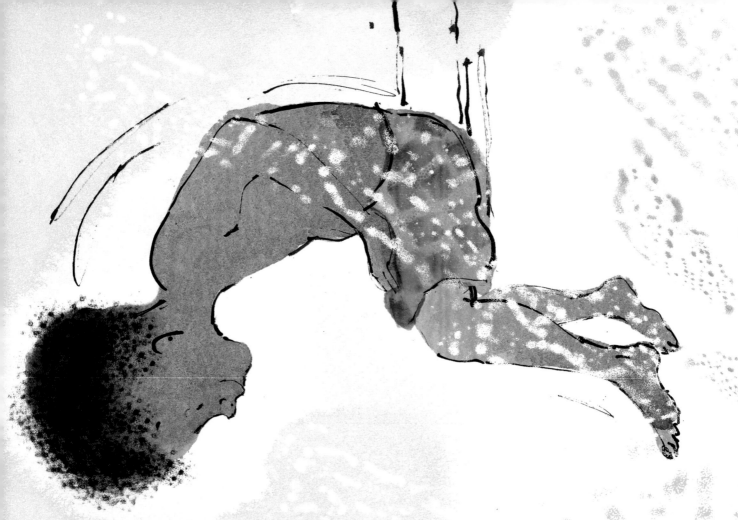

Dare to
trust...

Dare to
inspire!

Dare to do what hasn't been done.

Dare to be
second
to none.

Dare to see
when others
don't...

Dare to speak when others

won't.

Dare to reach out

and take
a chance.

Dare to sing,
dare to dance.

Dare to have
a hand to lend.

Dare to be your own best friend.

Dare
to enjoy
a silent
night.

Dare to be who you **truly are.**

A light
in the dark.

Be you...

a star!